Grade 5

Name

Date of exam

CW00349924

Contents

Editor for ABRSM: Richard Jones

Other pieces for this grade

First published in 2010 by ABRSM (Publishing) Ltd, a wholly owned subsidiary of ABRSM, 24 Portland Place, London W1B 1LU, United Kingdom

© 2010 by The Associated Board of the Royal Schools of Music

Music origination by Barnes Music Engraving Ltd
Cover by Økvik Design
Printed in England by Headley Brothers Ltd, The Invicta Press, Ashford, Kent

A:1

Air

Fourth movement from Partita No. 6 in E minor, BWV 830

J. S. Bach

J. S. Bach's E minor Partita (BWV 830) was originally dedicated to his wife Anna Magdalena – it is the second item in the *Clavierbüchlein* (little keyboard book) that he began compiling for her in 1725. Bach published the partita (i.e. suite) in 1730 and then reissued it within a collected edition of all six partitas in 1731. This collection, according to the original title-page, was intended 'for music lovers, to delight their spirits'. The *air* (literally 'tune') is one of the lightweight movement types that Bach inserted as intermezzi among the weightier dances of his suites, following the example of contemporary French composers. The rhythmic and metrical features of this air give it the character of a *tempo di gavotta*.
Source: *Clavier Übung*, Op. 1 (Leipzig, 1731)

Andante

from *Pièces de clavecin*, Op. 1

J. H. Fiocco

Joseph Hector Fiocco (1703–41) belonged to an Italian family of musicians that settled in Brussels. Primarily a keyboard player, he served as *sous-maître* at the court chapel and later as *maître de chapelle* at Antwerp Cathedral. His published harpsichord works owe much to those of François Couperin, for example in their fanciful movement titles and profuse ornamentation. In this Andante, non-triplet semiquavers, which first occur in b. 15, might be treated as *notes inégales* by assimilating them to the triplets. The florid RH melody requires a legato cantabile touch.

Source: *Pièces de clavecin*, Op. 1 (Brussels, 1730)

A:3

Menuet and Trio

Third movement from Sonata in B flat, Hob. XVI/2

Joseph Haydn

Menuet
[♩ = *c*.100]

D.S.

The Sonata in B flat, Hob. XVI/2, whose finale is given here, probably dates from around 1760 when the young Haydn was music director to Count Karl von Morzin. By that time Haydn's early keyboard works had already begun to circulate in Vienna. The dal segno indication applies only at the end of the whole movement (i.e. on the da capo): these last four bars are to be played again (perhaps *piano*) as a *petite reprise*.
Source: *Joseph Haydns Werke: Erste kritisch durchgesehene Gesamtausgabe*, Series 14, Vol. I, No. 2 (Leipzig, 1918)

Menuet D.C.

Miniature in D minor

No. 2 from *Dix miniatures en forme d'études*, Op. 8

A. F. Gedike

Aleksandr Fyodorovich Gedike (1877–1957) was a Russian composer who studied piano at the Moscow Conservatory and in 1909 was appointed professor there. He was also active as a concert pianist, both at home and abroad. In the Miniature in D minor, the basic dynamic is *piano*, but a considerable increase in tone is perhaps appropriate at the central climax in bb. 10–13.

rall. al fine

Elegy (In Autumn)

from *Scenes from Childhood*

Arvīds Žilinskis

The Latvian composer and pianist Arvīds Žilinskis (1905–93) was the son of a farmer and grew up in the woods and meadows, often helping his father herd his cattle and horses. He began learning the piano when displaced to Southern Ukraine at the end of the First World War. On his return to Latvia, he entered the Riga Conservatory at the age of 15. Following his graduation in 1933 he started to give concerts in schools, and wrote numerous songs and piano pieces that became very popular with children. Many of these pieces, including this autumnal elegy, reflect his love for the Latvian countryside. He taught for many years at the Latvian Conservatory and in all composed over 1,500 works, including ballets and operettas.

Andantino

No. 4 from *Fünf kleine Klavierstücke*, S. 192

Edited by Howard Ferguson

Franz Liszt

The Hungarian composer Franz Liszt (1811–86) was the greatest pianist of his day, and most of his piano music requires the skill of a virtuoso. But, as Howard Ferguson has pointed out, 'It's easy to forget that he also wrote short and beautiful pieces which are technically undemanding. Moreover, many of these are far more interesting musically than the typically brilliant works.' Among them are the *Fünf kleine Klavierstücke* (Five Little Piano Pieces), S. 192, written between 1865 and 1879 for Baroness Olga von Meyendorff. This Andantino, the fourth of the five pieces, was completed on 23 July 1876.

Source: autograph MS, The Library of Congress, Washington, DC, USA

© 1982 by The Associated Board of the Royal Schools of Music

Reproduced from Liszt: *Twenty-one Short Piano Pieces*, edited by Howard Ferguson (ABRSM)

Flood-Time

No. 5 from *Water Pieces*

C:1

Eric Thiman

Allegro con fuoco [♩. = *c*.144]

Eric Thiman (1900–75) was an English composer and organist who was appointed professor of harmony at the Royal Academy of Music in 1930. He taught in the Music Faculty of London University from 1952 and was organist and music director at the City Temple, London, from 1957.

It ain't necessarily so

from *Porgy and Bess*

Arranged by Richard Harris

Music and Lyrics by George Gershwin,
DuBose Heyward, Dorothy Heyward and Ira Gershwin

The American composer and pianist George Gershwin (1898–1937) and his brother and lyricist Ira Gershwin (1896–1983) built their reputation through the composition of songs and musicals, but George also wrote large-scale orchestral works, such as *Rhapsody in Blue*, which introduced jazz idioms into the concert hall. By the same token, the 'American folk opera' *Porgy and Bess*, with music and lyrics by George Gershwin, DuBose and Dorothy Heyward, and Ira Gershwin, which received its premiere on Broadway in 1935, introduced Afro-American folk music into opera. George and Ira Gershwin were gifted songwriters, and several of the songs from *Porgy and Bess* have become deservedly popular, including 'Summertime', 'I got plenty o' nuttin', and 'It ain't necessarily so', which is given here in a piano arrangement.

subito rit.   **Tempo primo**

Joyous March

No. 5 from *Enfantines*

Ernest Bloch

The Swiss-born composer Ernest Bloch (1880–1959) emigrated to America in 1916, becoming a US citizen in 1924. During the 1930s he lived mainly in Switzerland, but he returned to America at the end of 1938, taking up an appointment in 1940 as professor of music at the University of California, Berkeley. He composed in a very individual style that often featured Jewish and neoclassical elements. *Enfantines*, a set of ten pieces for children, dates from 1923.

Source: *Enfantines: Ten Pieces for Children* (New York: Carl Fischer, 1924)